G]

MW00769522

A Guide to Native Gemstones

Sharon & Bill Panczner   WULFENITE

A RENAISSANCE HOUSE PUBLICATION

© Copyright 1988 by Sharon & Bill Panczner. Printed in the United States of America. All rights reserved. This book or any parts thereof, may not be reproduced in any manner whatsoever without written permission of the publisher.

ISBN: 1-55838-097-3

RENAISSANCE HOUSE
A Division of Jende-Hagan, Inc.
541 Oak Street ~ P.O. Box 177
Frederick, CO 80530

'over photo of Malachite on Native Copper
'ourtesy Sharon & Bill Panczner

) 9 8 7 6 5 4

WELCOME

In the science of mineralogy there are over 2,40
different mineral species. Of this number, 640 hav
been found in Arizona. This number excludes the 1
minerals found in meteorites which have landed in th
state. Of the total, only about 100 are considere
gemstones, 12 of which are found in Arizona. The stat
has been credited with 48 mineral species being firs
discovered within its borders. From a geologic stand
point, minerals are nature's building blocks--naturall
occurring substances with a definite chemical an
internal make-up. Minerals can be found in man
varieties, exhibiting differences in form, color, or othe
properties. They are grouped in three basic division
Groups, e.g. garnet and feldspar; *Species,* e.g. quart
and gold; and *Varieties,* e.g. beryl variety aquamarine
Gemstones are extremely durable minerals that have
very high value for a small amount of material. The
are usually cut and polished to enhance their beaut
Rocks, on the other hand, are a combination of one o
more minerals and form into basic classes: igneou
sedimentary, and metamorphic. Each of these roc
types are formed in different conditions both at o
beneath the earth's surface.

Arizona is known as the copper state because of th
previously large production--Arizona's mines have pro
duced almost 50 *billion* pounds of copper, thus makin
it the leading copper producer in the U.S. The state'
official gemstone is turquoise, found in most of it
copper mines. Other Arizona gemstones include peri
dot, chrysocolla, jade and the quartz varieties amethys
smoky and clear rock crystal.

Mineral dealers, rock shops, gem, mineral, lapidar
clubs, and museums can be of great help in suggestin
collecting areas within the state. Permission is *alway*
required to collect from private lands; mines tha
appear to be abandoned are nevertheless owned b
someone. *All mines* are dangerous and great cautio
must be taken around them. *Never* go into a mine
collect only on the dumps.

To further aid your exploration of Arizona w
suggest these additional volumes in **The Arizon
Traveler** series:

CONTENTS

This work is dedicated to our two children, Shawna and Christopher, who at early ages traveled with us throughout Arizona. It was their enthusiasm that has been the major force for completion of this project.

Sharon & Bill Panczner   CALCITE

ARIZONA GEMS & MINERALS

The following is a brief listing of some of the more common minerals and gems and the counties in Arizona where they can be found. Mineral varieties are listed in **bold** type.

ARAGONITE: All counties

ARSENOPYRITE: Maricopa, Mohave, Pima, Santa Cruz, Yavapai

AZURITE: Cochise, Gila, Pima, Greenlee

BARITE: All counties

BERYL: Cochise, Graham, Mohave, Pima, Yavapai

BIOTITE: All counties

BORNITE: All counties

CALCITE: All counties

CERUSSITE: Cochise, Greenlee, Pima, Pinal, Santa Cruz

CHALCOCITE: Cochise, Coconino, Gila, Graham, Greenlee, Mohave, Pima, Pinal, Santa Cruz, Yavapai

CHALCOPYRITE: Cochise, Graham, Mohave, Pima, Pinal, Santa Cruz, Yavapai

CHRYSOCOLLA: All counties

CINNABAR: Gila, Maricopa, Pima, Pinal, Yavapai

COPPER: All counties

CUPRITE: All counties

DIOPTASE: Gila, Greenlee, Pima, Pinal, Santa Cruz, Yuma,

DOLOMITE: Cochise, Gila, Greenlee, Maricopa, Pima, Pinal, Santa Cruz, Yavapai

EPIDOTE: All counties

FELDSPAR: [Group name]

    Microcline: Cochise, Maricopa, Mohave, Pima, Yavapai

4

R.H. Perrill   WULFENITE

Orthoclase: Cochise, Maricopa, Mohave, Pima, Yavapai
Plagioclase: Cochise, Graham, Pima, Pinal
FLUORITE: Cochise, Gila, Graham, Greenlee, Maricopa, Mohave, Pima, Pinal, Santa Cruz, Yavapai, La Paz
GALENA: All counties
GARNET: [Group name]
  Pyrope: Apache
  Uvarolite: Mohave
  Almandine: Coconino, Mohave, Pima
  Spessartine: Mohave, Pinal, Yavapai
  Grossular: Cochise, Pima, Santa Cruz, Yavapai
  Andradite: Gila
GOETHITE: All counties
GOLD: All counties
GYPSUM: All counties
  Selenite: All counties
HALITE: Apache, Navajo, Cochise, Mohave, Pima, Pinal, Yavapai
HEMATITE: All counties
KYANITE: Maricopa, Yuma
MAGNETITE: Cochise, Coconino, Gila, Maricopa, Pima, Pinal, Santa Cruz, Yavapai
MALACHITE: All counties
MERCURY: Coconino, Gila, Maricopa, Mohave, Pinal, Yavapai
OBSIDIAN: [rock]
  Apache Tears: Mohave, Pinal, Maricopa, Yavapai
OLIVINE: All counties
  Peridot: Gila
OPAL: Santa Cruz
PYRITE: All counties

5

Sharon & Bill Panczner   MALACHITE IN CALCITE

QUARTZ: [Group name]
    Amethyst: Mohave, Navajo, Gila, Maricopa, Pinal, Pima, Santa Cruz
    Chalcedony: All counties
    Smoky: Santa Cruz, Navajo
    Petrified Wood: Apache, Navajo, Coconino, Pima, Santa Cruz
    Rock Crystal: All counties
SCHEELITE: Cochise, Gila, Graham, Maricopa, Mohave, Pima, Pinal, Santa Cruz, Yavapai, Yuma, La Paz
SIDERITE: Cochise, Gila, Greenlee, Mohave, Pima, Pinal, Santa Cruz, Yavapai, Yuma, La Paz
SILVER: All counties
SMITHSONITE: Cochise, Coconino, Gila, Graham, Greenlee, Pima, Pinal, Santa Cruz, Yavapai, Yuma, La Paz
SPHALERITE: Cochise, Gila, Graham, Mohave, Pima, Pinal, Santa Cruz, Yavapai
TOURMALINE: [Group name]
    Elbaite: Pinal, Pima, Maricopa
    Schorl: All counties
TURQUOISE: Cochise, Gila, Graham, Greenlee, Maricopa, Mohave Pima, Pinal, Yavapai
VANADINITE: Cochise, Coconino, Gila, Greenlee, Maricopa, Pima, Pinal, Santa Cruz, Yavapai, Yuma, La Paz
WAVELLITE: Gila, Mohave
WULFENITE: Cochise, Gila, Graham, Maricopa, Mohave, Pima, Pinal, Santa Cruz, Yavapai, Yuma, La Paz

6

Sharon & Bill Panczner   SELENITE VUG

Mineral & Gem Museums

Arizona's oldest gem and mineral museum is operated by the state at the Fair Grounds in Phoenix. It contains a large collection of Arizona ores, minerals, and gemstones. Also housed there is the Museum for the Arthur Flagg foundation, a private organization named for a past state mineralogist considered the father of rockhounding in Arizona.

Just west of Tucson in Tucson Mountain Park is the world famous Arizona-Sonora Desert Museum and its Congdon Earth Science Center. In addition to the collection of gems and minerals is a large three gallery walk-through man-made cave and mine, where the visitors can see actual pockets of minerals just as they were uncovered underground. On the University of Arizona campus in Tucson is the Mineral Museum of the Department of Geosciences, displaying an outstanding collection of minerals and gems, as well as Arizona rocks, ores, and fossils. Also on the campus is the history-oriented State Museum. Just across from the University is the Arizona Historical Society's Museum which contains a large walk-through man-made mine and a real stamp mill. There are a few minerals on display, but mostly for their historical note. New to

Sharon & Bill Panczner   AZURITE

the Tucson area is the Old Pueblo Museum located in the Foothills Mall. This small museum has a fine display of Arizona gems and minerals.

The Arizona Bank in Bisbee was once robbed not for its money, but for the mineral collection on display. Arizona State University in Tempe is renowned for its lab and display of meteorites. There are intriguing displays of minerals at Northern Arizona University and the Museum of Northern Arizona in Flagstaff. Petrified Forest and Grand Canyon National Parks and the Meteor Crater in northern Arizona should also be on the rockhound's itinerary.

Sharon & Bill Panczner   CERUSSITE

Vaughn Reichelderfer   PETRIFIED WOOD

THE PETRIFIED FOREST AREA

Located in northeastern Arizona is Petrified Forest National Park. Between 225 and 190 million years ago this area looked very much like today's Everglades. The sluggish streams and rivers of the region meandered past the low hills, swamps, marshes, ponds and oxbow lakes on their way to the sea. Along these watery paths were large trees reaching over 200 feet in height, early relatives of today's Norfolk Island Pine. Fallen trees and other plant materials collected as float and debris in the backwaters and lagoons and were quickly buried beneath the sediments. Through the slow geological process of petrification, the plant material was replaced cell by cell, making "replicas" of the original living plants with brightly colored quartz. The petrified trees we see today are the result of more than 60 million years of erosion. The quartz variety chalcedony which replaced the wood ranges in color shades of brown, gray, black, red, orange, yellow, white, and even blue. Occasionally malachite has been found replacing the wood, but this is rare. Sometimes the center of the petrified limbs are lined with crystals of amethyst, rock crystal or smoky quartz.

In the 1890s, a stamp mill was built in the Agate Bridge area of the park. The crushed petrified wood was shipped to a Denver abrasive factory for manufacturing into sandpaper! Also during this period, eastern jewelry firms had crews blasting large logs in search of cavities of rock and amethyst crystals to be fashioned into gems and used in jewelry. Recently on the northern edge of the Park near Chinle Point, the remains of the 225-million year old Plateosaur, the earliest datable dinosaur, were discovered.

Collecting within the Park is not allowed, but for a small fee you may collect on private lands nearby. Meteor Crater located near Canyon Diablo southwest of Winslow was created by a large meteorite which exploded just above the earth's surface millions of years ago. Lucky searchers near Canyon Diablo and the surrounding canyons might find fragments from this iron-nickel meteorite which created the crater.

9

Arizona Office of Tourism

OATMAN AREA

THE GRAND CANYON

There are few spots on earth to match the beauty and magnitude of the Grand Canyon. From a mineral stand-point, the Canyon has long produced small amounts of gold, silver, copper, and uranium from several of its mines. Most travelers are not aware that these mines, which are generally abandoned, exist within the Canyon. The one exception is the Orphan Mine, located on the Canyon's South Rim, which still produces uranium ore. This mine was granted special status by President Teddy Roosevelt to operate within the Park.

MOHAVE GOLD COUNTRY

This area of northwestern Arizona has been a major producer of gold and silver from several different mining camps and in more recent years a major producer of copper. Most of the gold and silver discoveries were made in the mid-1800s; each mining camp has stories of great bonanzas mixed with swindles in its historical records. Mining camps quickly grew and died as the ores played out. Ghost towns like Oatman and Goldfield still exist as reminders of past glories. But it was copper, not the precious metals, which would keep the region alive. In the mid-1950s with the discovery of a massive low-grade copper deposit at Mineral Park, a large open pit mine was developed. This site had been the home of several smaller precious metal underground mines. Despite the fact that Mineral Park Mine, the large open pit, has produced

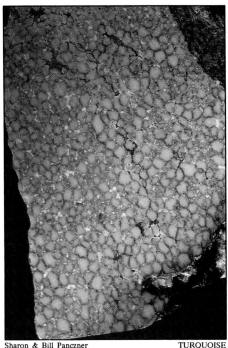

Sharon & Bill Panczner   TURQUOISE

millions of pounds of copper, it is best known for one particular copper mineral--turquoise. This turquoise has been rated among the best in the world. It was not uncommon to find large masses, up to 20-30 pounds of fine "spiderweb" turquoise. Usually the mineral is found in small veinlets which range from a pale to medium deep sky blue. It contains a fair amount of silica thus sporting a high shine when cut and polished. For nearly twenty years, the mining company which owns and operates the mine has subcontracted for the mining of turquoise and receives a commission on sales. At present, the Mineral Park Mine is not in operation due to the low price of copper, but as prices increase, it could reopen and turquoise as well as copper could be recovered. Other minerals which have been found here include: copper, azurite, malachite, chrysocolla, cuprite, selenite, calcite, wulfenite, wavellite, and quartz.

Southeast of Kingman in the Aquarius Mountain range is a feldspar deposit that has produced large pale blue crystal logs of beryl nearly 12 inches in diameter. Associated with the beryl are crystals of orthoclase, schorl, and biotite. Large garnet crystals up to two inches in diameter have been found near Toprock in the rocks of the Mohave Mountains west of Kingman. Usually the garnet crystals are small but occasionally large crystals are found.

Sharon & Bill Panczner   PYRITE COATED WITH HEMATITE

THE BRADSHAW REGION

The Bradshaw region in central Arizona is composed primarily of the Bradshaw Mountains. Since the arrival of man, this area has played an important role in mineral mining. Early Hunters and Gatherers were drawn to the area for minerals such as salt for preserving food and pigments for decorating pottery. In 1582, the Spanish conquistador Don Antonio de Espejo searched the Bradshaws for the rich mineral deposits about which the friendly natives told him. He discovered outcrops of silver in the rugged mountains and returned to Mexico in 1583 to tell officials of his discovery. In 1597, Don Juan Ornate, wanting to capitalize on Espejo's discoveries, organized an expedition led by Captain Marcos Farfan to the rich outcrops discovered earlier by Espejo. Farfan returned with "glowing reports" but due to the remoteness and timing, nothing was done to follow up the rich discoveries. Espejo has been given credit for naming the entire region Nuevo Mexico, a name that remained until 1863 when Arizona became a separate territory.

By the 1700s and early 1800s, rich silver and gold discoveries were being made in the mountain ranges and valleys. Names like Big Bug and Lynx Creeks, Walker, Rich Hill, Weaver, Peck, Crown King, Tip Top, Stanton, and Congress became famous mining areas within the region. Stories of rich bonanzas and schemes to defraud owners of their wealth fill the history books. The thousands of mines and prospects in the region are an important source of potential specimens for the interested collector.

Just north and west of Congress is Date Creek where quartz crystals up to four inches in length can be found. The crystals are often found with scepters of additional quartz crystals attached at the top of the main crystal. The quartz is slightly etched and often found with inclusions of green chlorite. Also found in the sands of the washes of the area are crystals of goethite replacing crystals of pyrite.

Further along U.S. 93 toward Kingman, just west and south of the Burro Creek crossing, weathering out of the local volcanic rocks are nodules of obsidian (Apache tears). Turn west off U.S. 93 just before the Burro Creek bridge and look in the bluffs above both sides of the road.

East of Congress near Rich Hill is the old mining camp of Stanton. In the wash below the main mine dump is a small outcrop of feldspar with crystals of microcline and orthoclase. Crystals of these minerals up to 12 inches in length and associated with biotite mica have been uncovered.

Bagdad, northwest of Prescott, has been a producer of copper since the early 1900s. Because of its remoteness and the high costs of shipping the ore, this deposit was not developed until the early 1920s. The open pit mine stopped operations in the 1970s when it became uneconomical due to low copper prices. The minerals that have been found here include chrysocolla, chrysocolla replacing crystals of azurite, azurite, malachite, and fine crystals of calcite. Southwest of Bagdad is another fairly large feldspar deposit which has produced crystals of schorl, beryl, mica, and garnet. Quartz variety chalcedony, both green and blue, have been found along the Santa Maria River southwest of the bridge on the main highway from Bagdad to Hillside. Southwest of Prescott is Copper Basin where, in years past, gold and copper were produced from the district's mines. Travelers can still find azurite, malachite and chrysocolla on most of the dumps and if lucky, pan a little gold from the area streams.

The Bradshaw Mountains have been a good producer of gold. The Lynx and Big Bug Creeks were two of the bigger producers of this precious metal. It is still possible to pan successfully in almost any of the mountain streams. Occasionally someone will find a large (up to an ounce) gold nugget. Along the Big Bug Creek, several of the old mine dumps have yielded fine crystals of pyrite, up to several inches.

Just north of Meyer along the right side of the highway to Prescott is an old quarry that was operated for onyx. Although not in operation, it still produces good cutting grade onyx. Located on the eastern slopes of the Bradshaws in Peck Canyon are the Peck and Swastika mines. This area has produced fine specimens of several different silver minerals. With effort the mine dumps could still yield a few specimens of interest.

Arizona Office of Tourism   JEROME

JEROME/VERDE VALLEY/RIM COUNTR

In 1583, Don Antonio de Espejo was the first European to view the rich mineralized outcrops on Mingus Mountain which hundreds of years later would become the famous mining camp of Jerome. Al Seiber located the first claim and named it after the color of the outcrop, El Verde. Because of its remoteness from the nearest railroad spur 176 miles away, the mining district developed very slowly. In 1888, Senator W.A. Clark from Butte, Montana became active in the developing mining district. Over the next 40 years the mines of Jerome would net him a profit of over $60 million. In 1919 a small open pit was developed along with the extensive underground mining operations. Clark's United Verde Mine set a world record as the richest mine to be owned by one individual. In 1935 Phelps Dodge acquired the mining properties within the district, but not before more than 20 million tons of ore had been mined. The yield was two billion pounds of copper, nearly a million ounces of gold, and almost 35 million ounces of silver. Phelps Dodge gambled on an area which had no surface indications of mineralization and developed the new United Verde Extension Mine.

One of the unique features of the mines of Jerome is the great fire which burned more than 50 years within the rich sulfide orebody. A series of extremely rare minerals formed during the fire within the orebody, but these are seldom seen or available.

The mines started to close in the 1960s, and by the 1970s operations were silent. The mining camp, built on the side of Mingus Mountain 2,000 feet above the

14

Verde Valley, is a picturesque community today. Mineral specimens of interest here are calcite, aragonite, azurite, and malachite.

In the valley south and west of Camp Verde along the Verde River is the Salt Mine. This location has been worked since 900 A.D. by the Indians of the valley for salt (halite) to preserve their foods. The mine was worked in the mid 1900s, not for halite but for the associated minerals used in the manufacturing of paper. To the collector, this location is noted for the halite which sometimes contains blue "clouds" floating inside. Small crystals of glauberite and gypsum replacing glauberite crystals are also found there. Several years ago, stalactites of thenardite and mirabilite were found. Use caution around the open pit mine.

The volcanic rocks of the Verde Valley often contain cavities of crystals of different zeolites, which can be found by the patient rockhound.

East of Payson just off the road to Kohls Ranch at Diamond Point, small water-clear doubly terminated quartz crystals can be found weathering out of the soil just below the fire control tower. A little further down the Kohls Ranch road just above the land-fill waste dump, black and white chalcedony (agate) has been found. This agate cuts and polishes fairly well and looks like zebra skin. Just before Kohls Ranch, turn left from the main highway onto the control road. Travelers can find attractive pink to rose red fossils in the limestone rocks along the road. These fossils are of marine life that lived in this region millions of years ago.

CLIFTON/MORENCI

After working placer deposits along the San Francisco River in 1863-64, Henry Clifton discovered rich copper outcrops in the cliffs of a remote canyon of eastern Arizona. Because of the Apache Indian's constant raids, development of the deposit was slow. By the early 1870s, the district had begun to grow with new mines and even a smelter to process the ore. One of the principal partners approached Phelps Dodge Company for money to expand operations at Clifton/Morenci. In 1881, because of the impressive report of the ore zones of Morenci, the advancement of funds was approved for the Detroit Copper Company and by 1895 Phelps Dodge was in full control of the operations at Morenci.

The Arizona Copper Company, which had been working on the opposite end of the ore zone at Clifton, expanded its operations and produced good profits for its shareholders. In 1921, Phelps Dodge took over Arizona Copper, controlling almost all of the district's

Sharon & Bill Panczner   AZURITE

mines. Phelps Dodge decided to place its efforts on the Morenci Mine, and during the late 1930s expanded the operation into a large open-pit mine. By the 1940s it was the state's largest, a title still held today. During the 1950s and '60s Phelps Dodge averaged about $100 million a year in copper production from here. Like other copper mines in Arizona in the early 1980s, because of the depressed copper economics, mining all but stopped. In past years, Phelps Dodge has done exploration work at nearby Metcalf, but this project has virtually stopped due to low copper prices.

Minerals from this district include the more common copper minerals, most notably azurite and malachite. The exploration at Metcalf produced some of the finest azurite and malachite specimens ever found in Arizona. It is almost impossible to collect in the area except by buying specimens from local dealers. This region has some of the best collecting sites for quartz variety chalcedony (agate).

At Mulligan Peak in Limestone Canyon, banded agate nodules of deep purple to lavender have been found. Another site, known as the Clifton Fire Agate Field, is southeast of Ward Canyon. Both sites are very scenic even if one finds little to collect. Another collecting site is an area northeast of Safford. To the west of the main highway going from Safford to Clifton is a field of fire agate. Southwest of Duncan, west of the main highway from Duncan to Lordsburg, is a location probably producing the finest fire agate in Arizona. In summer, watch for rattlesnakes in this rocky area. Respect private property and close gates behind you.

16

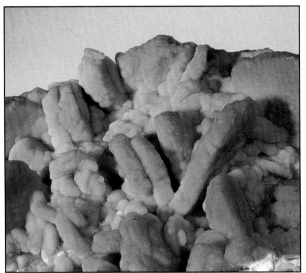

R.H. Perrill   CHRYSOCOLLA AFTER AZURITE

GLOBE/MIAMI

Ultimately one of Arizona's major copper producing areas, it was not copper that began Globe/Miami's development. North of the present city of Globe, in the Apache Mountains, silver had been known since 1869. It was said that the Apache Indians mined this silver to make bullets. Several of General George Crook's soldiers were shot by the Indians with silver bullets.

Silver was discovered at Richmond Basin on the north side of the Apache Mountains in 1873 as float lying on the surface. One of the first claim locators described the large silver nuggets as being the size of cantaloupes, saying, "Why man she's as big as the whole globe," and then named his claim Globe after the silver spheres. Mines began to develop here and on the south side of the mountain range at McMillenville, but because this was at the edge of the Apache Indian Territory, raids by the Indians were common and mining development slowed.

Interest in minerals quickly turned 20 miles south to the rich new copper discovery made during the late 1870s and early 1880s. In 1892 Phelps Dodge and Co. bought the United Globe Mine, and in 1903, the Old Dominion Mine. Other mining camps quickly developed around the surrounding mines and the names of Miami and Inspiration began to appear on the local maps. In the early 1900s, Miami Copper Co. was formed to mine and process the low-grade copper ore of the area.

Shortly thereafter, Inspiration Copper Co. and Live

Sharon & Bill Panczner CHRYSOCOLLA & MALACHITE

Oak Development Co. merged to form the Inspiration Consolidated Copper Co. and mined ore from the Inspiration and Live Oak Mines. Production continued at Globe from the Old Dominion Mine, and the district's total output from the early 1900s to the 1920s was more than one billion pounds of copper. By the late 1930s and early 1940s most of the mines around Globe had closed, but the Miami and Inspiration mines still were in operation. During this time the mines underwent short periods where they slowed or even stopped operations. In the 1920s, exploration began for other copper deposits in the area and the large low-grade deposit was uncovered at Castle Dome, a few miles west of Miami.

With the increased demand for copper during World War II, the Castle Dome Mine was developed and began production. The Copper Cities Mine, just north of the Miami, also began production. Like most copper districts of Arizona, the mines have closed since the downturn in the copper economy.

Minerals from these mines include: chrysocolla, azurite, malachite, cuprite, and calcite. The chrysocolla is the finest found in the state. Much of this deep blue mineral contains a high amount of silica, and when cut and polished will yield beautiful gemstones.

Just north of Claypool, between Miami and Globe, is a small mine which for several years produced the metal vanadium. The Apache Mine has produced some of Arizona's finest crystals of bright blood red vanadinite. This mineral can be found associated with quartz, descloizite, and mottramite. The mine is now

18

Sharon & Bill Panczner   VANADINITE

operating as a small open pit and specimens can be purchased at local rock and mineral shops.

East of Globe on U.S. 60 on the Apache Indian Reservation is the small village of Peridot, named after the mineral found in the nearby mesa. This location is closed to collecting but you can buy peridot from the Indians at the trading post in Peridot. Gemstones of nearly 50 carats have been cut from here. They are a fine green color, with larger stones of the dark green color. Much of the peridot from here is dark and referred to as "sleepy" due to the hazy inclusions.

Just off the Reservation and east of the Coolidge Dam is a dirt road leading south to Stanley Butte. This location has long been a producer of fine andradite garnet crystals, some almost two inches in diameter and usually found in clusters. Also in the area are slender crystals of quartz of both varieties amethyst and rock crystal. Some of these crystals are up to five inches in length. The Apache's are now claiming ownership of this area and it is presently closed to collecting.

Just west of Stanley Butte near Kelly Canyon is an agate deposit and several abandoned mines with dumps that have yielded small pinkish-white crystals of barite. North of Globe, near the small town of Young, is a black jade location. This material cuts and polishes very nicely and is available at most of the rock and mineral shops of the area. North and east of Globe in the Salt River Canyon is a large deposit of serpentine asbestos. Once an active mining area for this mineral, the mines are now closed.

Sharon & Bill Panczner   BARITE

SUPERIOR/WINKELMAN AREA

This old mining area of central Arizona has produced many outstanding mineral specimens. The region's northern end is at Superior and the southern end at Winkelman. In between are the mining camps of Ray and Hayden. Silver was discovered near what is now Superior in the mid 1870s by a soldier building a road in the Pinal Range. He died mysteriously before telling of his discovery in full detail. In 1875, silver was rediscovered and on March 22, the Silver King Mine opened. The mine was not long-lived, but it was a steady producer of ore. The area was considered by most prospectors to have too little silver and too much copper in the ore.

A New York mining company began to develop the Silver Queen Mine, and by 1882 had sunk a shaft to the 400 foot level. In 1910, the newly organized Magma Copper Company took over operations at the Silver Queen and renamed it the Magma Mine. By 1912, the main shaft had been developed to a depth of 800 feet. That same year, the townsite of Superior was surveyed and construction began. Mine development continued down to the 2,000 foot level, and several new shafts were sunk to handle the rich ore being mined at the great depth. As the years passed, the Magma was developed to depths of over 5,000 feet to reach the rich copper orebody. Economics and two World Wars caused interruptions, but Magma Copper Co. continued to modernize both its underground, surface and milling operations. Finally in the early 1980s economics

Sharon & Bill Panczner   NATIVE COPPER

stopped the mining operation completely.

Minerals from the mines of Superior today are limited to those brought out by the miners. It is impossible for collectors to gather specimens at any of the dumps or abandoned mines. Minerals for which the Magma Mine is famous includes barite, chalcocite, bornite and calcite. These crystals of calcite and barite are among the best in Arizona.

Just south and west of Superior is the famous Apache Tear mine. This small open pit was originally dug for perlite, a volcanic rock that contains obsidian, and the mine is now open for collecting obsidian. Apache Tears are nodules of this black transparent volcanic rock. The stone is easy to cut and polish and is a favorite of beginning lapidarists. In the same area one can find petrified wood.

South of Superior, another mining district began development in the early 1870s. The claims were sold in 1898 to the English firm of Ray Copper Mines Ltd., but it was not until 1906 that the area was developed on a large scale by the newly reorganized Ray Consolidated Copper Company. The orebody was large but the copper content was low-grade. With the use of new technology the mine became highly profitable. The underground operation was abandoned and a large open pit developed. In the early 1960s the old townsite of Ray was destroyed when the pit was enlarged. Presently the mine, like most other copper operations in Arizona, is closed due to economics.

Collecting at the Ray Mine is limited to field trips conducted by the Phoenix and Tucson area mineral and

21

Sharon & Bill Panczner   WULFENITE

gem clubs. Minerals found there include copper, cup-rite, chalcotrichite, chrysocolla, calcite, dioptase, mala-chite and azurite. Several years ago many pockets of chrysocolla pseudomorphs were uncovered with crys-tals nearly four inches in length. In the early 1960s, several pockets of cuprite with crystals nearly 1/2 inch long were found. These crystals were associated with hair-like needles of the cuprite variety chalcotrichite. Some of the most outstanding crystals of copper, up to five inches in length, were discovered in the mid 1970s. Some of these crystals were covered with malachite and a few were also naturally twisted like a drill.

Another location at the edge of the mine's north waste rock dump is a small wash that has cut through the local rock, exposing large two inch crystals of orthoclase and alpha quartz. The alpha quartz crystals are less than 1/2 inch in size, have etched surfaces and are doubly terminated. Because this area is unsafe, it has been closed to collecting, but some of the local mineral shops may still have a specimen or two for sale.

Just north and east of Hayden is the Seventy-Nine Mine, a lead/silver mine located as a claim in 1879. It has been a small producer compared to other Arizona mines, but an outstanding specimen-producing mine for the collector. This location is most noted for its yellow wulfenite crystals with red dots in the crystal centers and bright blue needle-like crystals of auri-chalcite. Other minerals of note from here include smithsonite and rosasite. Collecting is not permitted at the mine so specimens must be obtained from the local mineral dealers or collectors. East and north of Hay-den at Christmas is the Christmas Mine, noted for specimens of kinoite and dioptase. This mine is closed to collecting but on occasion, mineral and gem societies are allowed into the mine on field trips.

Sharon & Bill Panczner   AMETHYST

PHOENIX AREA

East of Phoenix, high in the Mazatal Mountain range, is an area called Four Peaks. Near the top of one of the peaks is a mine that has yielded the best amethyst found in Arizona. The amethyst is found in the vugs or "pockets" of quartzite. Crystal points have been found up to 10 inches in length, but most are smaller. The vugs are usually small, but some nearly six feet in diameter have been found. The color is a deep burgundy, making these crystal tips very desirable for faceting. The mine was operated several years ago, but is not in operation now. Elevation at the mine is about 8,000 feet and the hike up is rather strenuous.

On the west side of the Mazatal Mountains, down on the valley floor near the small town of Sunflower, is an old mercury mining district. The mines, located just east of the road to Payson, are presently not in operation. Small micro-size crystals of the mercury mineral cinnabar can be found, but they are considered rare from this location.

In Phoenix there are two mineral locations of note. The first, on the northeast side of the city, is along the south side of Mummy Mountain where large crystals of schorl have been found. Unfortunately, houses have been built on the sites where the crystals were found. The second location, on the northern side of the city, is in Squaw Peak Park. As you hike up the trail to the summit, watch for crystals of pale blue kyanite. Some have been found up to four inches in length.

Northwest of Phoenix near Morristown on the road

MARYLAND CARTOGRAPHICS, INC.
Columbia, Maryland 21045

NEVADA

UT

Littlefield

Kaibab Indian Reservation

Freede

Jacob L

Kaibab

Fo

Lake Mead

Lake Mead National Recreation Area

Colorado

River

Kanab

Creek

Lake Mead National Recreation Area

Havasupai Indian Reservation

G

Hualapai Indian Reservation

93

3

66

Seligman

40

Ash Fork

Ka

89

Kingman

68

40

3

93

Prescott

CALIFORNIA

Fort Mohave Indian Reservation

4

Bagdad

National

Prescott

Fores

4

Lake Havasu City

Hillside

96

Kirkland

0   10   20   30   40   50 Miles

0   10   20   30   40   50 Kilometers

Bill Williams River

4

Congress

4

Colorado

River

95

Parker

Colorado River Indian Reservation

72

Aguila

71

Wickenburg

9

74

Vicksburg

60

10

10

60

89

Ehrenberg

10

Gle

Yuma

Proving

Kofa

National

Wildlife

Refuge

Tonopah

10

Buckeye

11

Grounds

Sonora

85

Yuma

Desert

10

Gila Bend

8

Welton

Tacna

Dateland

Gila

River

85

San Luis

Luke Air Force Range

Cabeza Prieta
National Wildlife
Refuge

12

Ajo

Why

8

Organ Pipe
Cactus
National
Monument

85

Lukeville

1   The Petrified Forest Area
2   The Grand Canyon
3   Mohave Gold Country
4   The Bradshaw Region
5   Jerome, Verde Valley
     and the Rim
6   Clifton/Morenci
7   Globe/Miami
8   Superior/Winkelman Area
9   The Phoenix Area
10 The Vulture/Harquahala
     Area
11 The Yuma Region
12 Ajo
13* The Tucson Area
14 Tiger

15 Empire Mountains
16 Tombstone
17 Pearce/Cortland/Gleeson
     Area
18 Huachuca Mountains
19 The Chiricahua Region
20 Bisbee
21 Washington Camp Region
22 The Santa Rita Mountains
23 Arivaca Area

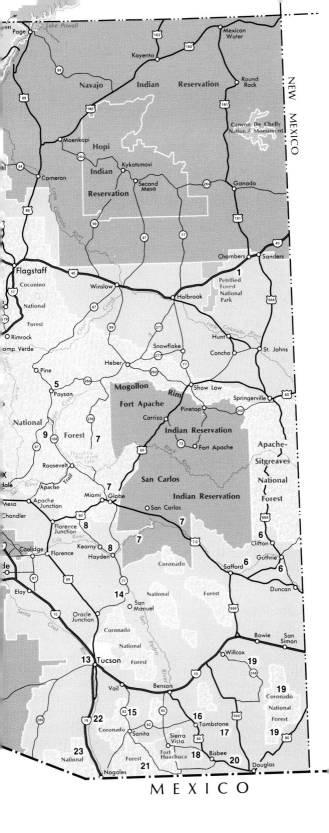

Kendal Atchison   ARRASTRA

to Castle Hot Springs is the White Picacho mining district. This is a pegmatite region that is characterized by the high concentration of minerals containing rare earth metals. The area has not been worked for several years and the mine dumps would have to be overturned to expose new material. Local minerals would include most of the feldspar and mica groups.

THE VULTURE/HARQUAHALA AREA

In 1853, Henry Wickenburg discovered surface gold south of Rich Hill near the Hassayampa River. Legend has it that he threw a rock at his reluctant burro that had stopped because of vultures circling over head. Discovering that the rock he threw contained gold, he traced it back to its source and filed claim on the location, naming it for the birds. Soon many arrastras or mills were built to process the ore, 12 miles south along the Hassayampa River. During its heyday, the mine was noted for the excessive amount of "high-grading" or the illegal removal of the ores by the miners.

One of the more famous miners who worked at the Vulture was Jacob Walz of "Lost Dutchman Mine" fame. To conceal his stealing from his employer at the Vulture, Walz would enter Phoenix from the east and tell of his great discovery of the "Lost Dutchman Mine." The mine operated steadily until 1872 when the ore veins began to pinch off and became too low grade to mine. It reopened in the mid-1900s and closed for good at the beginning of WW II.

R.H. Perrill WULFENITE

Yellow wulfenite crystals up to two inches across can be found here, and occasionally small flakes of gold. The mine is closed to collecting.

Northwest of the Vulture Mine, obsidian nodules (apache tears) are found weathering out of the local volcanic rocks. These Apache Tears are banded and can be cut and polished into interesting cat's eyes.

South of the Vulture Mine is Fourth of July Butte and Saddle Mountain which contain deposits of quartz variety chalcedony. This material when cut and polished exhibits colors that look like "fire"--hence the name Fire Agate. A few miles south and west is another famous collecting site, the Rowley Mine. This silver/lead mine, like many others in the state, is better known for its production of mineral specimens than ore. Its history dates from the late 1800s to the mid 1900s. It lies in ruins today, but is not abandoned. The owners, who live in California, have posted the property. They occasionally allow clubs on the dumps to collect, and good specimens are still found, but one has to work to find them. Minerals from this location include wulfenite, mimetite, chrysocolla and barite. The wulfenite has been found as paper-thin bright orange-red crystals up to 1-1/2 inches wide. Sometimes the crystals are found associated with bright yellow needle-like crystals of mimetite. Agate has been found in the volcanic rocks just southwest of the mine on the south side of the Painted Rock mountains. The agate field is east of the road leading back to the highway toward Gila Bend. Nodules from here range up to three inches in size and are gray banded.

Sharon & Bill Panczner   CHRYSOCOLLA PSEUDOMORPH

Further north and west of these locations are the Harquahala Mountains and the site of the Harquahala or Bonanza Mine. This site may also have been discovered by Henry Wickenburg, apparently before he discovered gold at the Vulture Mine. It appears that Wickenburg discovered gold here and was on his way to file this claim when he found richer gold ore at the Vulture site. In 1888, the Bonanza Mine began mining operations on the gold ore. In 1891 a stamp mill was added to increase output of the ore and gold recovery. Two years later another company sank a new shaft and made improvements to the mill. The mine has a history of short periods of operation separated by long periods of idle time. In the early 1920s, a recently graduated mining engineer worked on deepening the main shaft. He later quit his job at the mine to go into politics and eventually became President of the U.S.--Herbert Hoover.

To the collector, this location is better known for the copper minerals which were found there in the mid-1960s. A huge bench was cut on the hill above the mine, exposing a large vein of dioptase. Although crystals were small, coverage on the rock was very large, up to four or five inches in diameter. Several rare copper minerals were found with malachite and chrysocolla.

Sharon & Bill Panczner   WULFENITE

THE YUMA AREA

North of Yuma and just a few miles east of the Colorado River are many small silver/lead mines. One of them, the Red Cloud, is world famous to collectors. The Red Cloud was discovered in the early 1880s and operated on and off for many years. Presently it is closed to the collector and a watchman lives on the site. The mineral most frequently collected here is the blood red wulfenite crystal. Crystals have been found just over two inches in width with bright shiny surfaces. Rock and mineral dealers in Arizona usually have a few wulfenite crystals from the Red Cloud in their stock. Just north of Yuma on the road through the Yuma proving grounds is a small area where petrified iron wood can be found. Unfortunately this area is closed to the collector because its location in the bombing range makes it extremely dangerous.

AJO

Mineral outcrops have been known by the Spanish for many years, but because of its remote location, Ajo was never fully explored. Not until 1854 was the area "rediscovered" by American engineers. It is thought that Ajo was the first mining area to have produced copper in Arizona. Near the surface the ores were very rich, but as depth increased, ore grades decreased. Water and the high cost of shipping the ore created problems. The St. Louis Copper Company started

R.H. Perrill   NATIVE COPPER

operations at Ajo, but soon went bankrupt.

Cornelia Copper, formed by a few of the original St. Louis partners, secured capitol and obtained some of the latest smelter equipment for their Ajo operation. The Calumet and Arizona acquired options on Cornelia Copper's stock and in 1911 discovered a large, low grade ore body. By the beginning of WW I, they were ready to meet the demands for copper needed in the war.

In 1929, the New Cornelia and Calumet and Arizona merged to form the Calumet and Arizona Company. Two years later, Phelps Dodge bought out the Calumet and Arizona, becoming the operator of the Ajo mining operations. The New Cornelia Mine became part of the New Cornelia branch of Phelps Dodge. The operations were modernized both in the enlargement of the open pit and at the smelter. As with most copper operations within Arizona, Ajo is presently closed due to economics.

Important minerals from Ajo are native copper with crystals up to eight inches in size; crystals of azurite up to two inches; malachite replacing azurite with crystals up to two inches; and ajoite and papagoite. The latter two can be cut and polished with fine results. Phelps Dodge Company does not allow collecting in the open pit, so mineral specimens must come through miners to the local rock and mineral dealers.

R.H. Perrill   WULFENITE

THE TUCSON AREA

In the 1970s, Tucson was the hub of the copper mining industry. The mines, a short distance away, almost surrounded the city. There mining operations yielded millions of pounds of copper, but few specimens of interest to collectors. Specimens of note include: small crystals of native copper "floating" in water-clear selenite, azurite, malachite, chrysocolla, and turquoise. Most of these mines are presently closed because of copper prices.

Of interest to the collector is a small silver/gold mine in the northern end of the Tucson Mountains, the Old Yuma Mine. This property like many others in the state has had small production records, and is more famous as a collecting site than for its mining production. Large crystals of orange wulfenite and red vanadinite have been found here. In the mid-1970s a large pocket of vanadinite yielded blood-red crystals up to two inches long. Earlier, a large pocket had been uncovered yielding bright orange wulfenite crystals, some just over two inches wide and clustered in crystal aggregates nearly six inches wide. The mine is currently closed to collecting because of exploration for gold and silver being conducted there.

R.H. Perrill   CERUSSITE

TIGER

Gold, discovered here in 1879, was the cause of the great rush to file mining claims within the newly developing Top Hat Mining District. In the early 1900s, other metals were discovered and recovered from the ores. These included molybdenum, vanadium, lead, zinc and later copper. In the 1930s, mining stopped completely within the district, resuming later in the decade, and continued until 1953. The owners, Magma Copper Company, moved operations just south to the larger copper orebody and the new San Manuel Mine. There was some activity on the surface near the Mammoth Mine in the late 1970s, for silica used for flux in the copper smelter at San Manuel.

Famous mines of the district include the Mohawk, Mammoth and St. Anthony, which eventually connected underground and was then referred to as the Mammoth/St. Anthony Mine.

The town of Tiger which developed near the mines was totally removed in 1954 and the miners and their families were moved to Mammoth or to the new town of San Manuel.

This area is closed to collecting, but once or twice a year the local mineral and lapidary clubs have field trips to collect on the old dumps. The list of minerals from here is very extensive. Mineral specimens from the mine are very showy and can be found in nearly all museums around the world. The more common minerals are wulfenite, vanadinite, dioptase and cerussite.

Sharon & Bill Panczner   WULFENITE ON DIOPTASE

EMPIRE MOUNTAINS

In the Empire mountains southeast of Tucson is the site of the Total Wreck Mine and several other smaller mines and prospects. The Total Wreck Mine started production in 1879 and operated until the early 1900s for lead and silver. It then operated intermittently for the next 20 years when it was finally abandoned.

Recently the Total Wreck was sold and the new owners have not announced plans for development; it is presently closed to collecting. Along the west side of the ridge line are a series of small mine dumps, all worthy of exploration. On the far south end of the ridge a road leads to a mine called the Half Wreck, whose dumps make excellent collecting sites. To reach this area, take the third dirt road that turns east from the road to Sonoita. Close all gates behind you and do not go on posted lands that surround some of the mines.

Important minerals from this area include wulfenite, vanadinite, descloizite, calcite aurichalcite and quartz. All of these can be found as crystallized specimens. This area has been overlooked by most hobbyists and collectors because of its small size and location.

East of the Empire Mountains just beyond the Apache Powder plant near St. David, weathering from the low hills are crystal clusters of gypsum variety selenite. The tan crystals can be found in rose shaped groups up to four inches in diameter and are often referred to as desert roses.

Thomas J. Barbre

TOMBSTONE

In all of Arizona's history probably no other mining camp is more often mentioned than Tombstone. The first mine, about five miles west of town, was located in 1857, but because of Indian raids, the district didn't begin to develop until 1877. In the early 1880s, Tombstone was Arizona's largest city, with a population of about 4,000, of which only 700 worked in the mines or mills. As the district expanded and the mines went deeper for their silver/lead ores, water became a problem. In the mid-1880s, the future of the district's mines looked bright. But silver prices dropped, and as the depth of the mines increased, so did the level of water in them until operations slowly began to close. What mines did stay open expanded their workings above the water level.

In the early 1900s, the mines began to reopen. New pumps were installed which could handle the increasing problem of water. Now the mines could go deeper into the ore zone. But as they increased depth, the costs of operations greatly increased. New milling technology was applied to the ores of Tombstone with great success. During WW I, the manganese found in the district's ores was needed by the Allies for the special steels used in the war effort. By the end of the war, the mines of Tombstone began to run out of ore and by

Sharon & Bill Panczner AZURITE

1929 they were closed again. Sporadic production took place during the 1930s and 40s before the mines finally closed for the last time.

In the middle 1980s, operations resumed on a very limited basis as compared to the bonanza days of old. The mines had yielded almost $38 million in production since 1879. Noted mines of the district include the Contention, Grand Central, Bunker Hill, Emerald, Congress and the Lucky Cuss. There is little or no collecting in the area because of all the mine dumps being reworked for ore. Specimens from here are rarely seen except in museums. Most of the more common silver minerals have been found here.

BILLY CLANTON
TOM M?LAURY
FRANK M?LAURY
MURDERED
on the streets
of
TOMBSTONE
1881

TOM
McLAURY
Killed
Oct 26 1881

Arizona Office of Tourism   TOMBSTONE'S BOOT HILL CEMETERY

R.H. Perrill

PEARCE/COURTLAND/GLEESON ARE

This mineralized region is divided into three areas, Pearce to the north, Courtland in the middle and Gleeson to the south. Pearce was a silver/gold area discovered in 1895 with the location of the Commonwealth and Pearce Mines. This mining camp was backed financially by Richard Penrose, a mining engineer from Cripple Creek, Colorado. The mines operated until the early 1930s before the price of silver dropped. They now lie in ruins and the dumps are nearly covered with desert vegetation.

Courtland and Gleeson are usually associated together, both in their history and mineralogy. Turquoise has been known from the Courtland area since before 1877, when the first mining claim was filed on the area. The Indians of the region had worked the surface for that copper bearing gemstone. Because of the hostility of the local Apache Indians, the district developed slowly, but by the late 1890s it began to expand and develop. Railroads were established in the region to carry in supplies and bring out the metals being mined and processed. The copper/lead/silver ores could run rich, then turn to very low grade in the space of a few feet, however. The Defiance Mine, as well as others in the district, operated sporadically through the mid-1900s.

This area is well known to hobbyists and collectors for several different minerals. From the Courtland area, turquoise can still be found on the dumps on the west side of Turquoise Ridge. From Gleeson and the Defiance Mine come wulfenite, smithsonite, aurichalcite and rosasite. The wulfenite that was found in the early 1950s consisted of opaque-butterscotch colored crystals up to one inch in width. The recent wulfenite

36

Stanley Zamonski

crystals are paper thin, water clear and yellow. They were found up to widths of one inch. The dumps of the mines still produce specimens, but one has to be very careful of the open mine workings leading underground. Safety must always be practiced when around abandoned mine workings and *please* respect private property within this district. A couple of the land owners in the area are said to have shot first and talked later! Recently several collectors were arrested while collecting underground and spent a night in the Tombstone jail. Their specimens were confiscated by the local sheriff.

.H. Perrill   WULFENITE

Sharon & Bill Panczner GOLD

HUACHUCA MOUNTAINS

This mountain range starts in Arizona and ends south of the border in Mexico. At the northern end of the range is the old but still active Cavalry post of Fort Huachuca. The entire mountain range is highly mineralized with many small mines scattered throughout.

The Reef Mine near the top of the east side of the Huachucas was operated for gold, and in the mid-1900s for tungsten. Several years ago a large nugget of gold was found below the mine in one of the many washes of the area. Occasionally scheelite can still be found on the mine's dump.

Clusters of water clear quartz crystals have been found throughout the entire mountain range. The crystals have ranged up to four inches in length, in clusters up to a foot in diameter. On the west side of the Huachucas are several small mines, prospects, and the old ghost town of Sunnyside. There is a caretaker living at the site who loves to tell stories of the area.

THE CHIRICAHUA REGION

In the southeastern corner of the state are the Chiricahua Mountains, one of Arizona's more interesting mountain ranges. Not only does it contain unusual plant and animal life, it is also the site of several mineral locations. On the northeast side of the range is the old town of Hill Top and the Hill Top Mine. This lead/silver mine in the mid 1930s and again in the 1950s produced many fine specimens of butterscotch yellow wulfenite crystals. These opaque crystals were up to two inches across, on a white calcite and limestone matrix. Some of the matrix specimens were

Chiricahua National Monument

almost 30 inches in diameter.

On the southeast side of the Chiricahuas is Crystal Cave which is lined with quartz crystal points. Unfortunately over the years much of the cave was ruined and today has lost some of its glamour, but it is still of interest. Rangers at the Chiricahua National Monument, where the cave is located, will give tours.

In the next mountain range to the north and west, The Dos Cabezas Mountains, is the location of another gold/tungsten deposit. The Cohen Mine was first worked for gold and then for the tungsten mineral scheelite. Orange-red crystals of scheelite more than a foot in size have been found, often attached to quartz crystals.

Sharon & Bill Panczner   GOLD

39

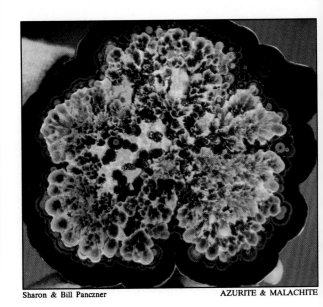

Sharon & Bill Panczner

AZURITE & MALACHITE

BISBEE

The discovery of outcrops of ore in the Mule Mountains is credited to three U.S. Cavalry Scouts from Fort Huachuca in the summer of 1877. Because of their inability to work the claim, they grubstaked a Tombstone prospector, George Warren, to undertake the job. Warren prospected the area carefully and filed several more claims in 1878 for copper and lead. One of these would become world famous as the Copper Queen Mine. Because of his love for whiskey, Warren lost his Copper Queen claim betting on the outcome of a foot race between himself and a horseback rider.

The town of Bisbee was born in 1880 and on April 2, 1881, the Copper Queen Mining Company began removing ore from the Copper Queen claim. On several occasions during the early years of mining, the rich copper ore would begin to run out. Orders would be given to stop work, but the miners would work until the end of their shifts. Just as they were about to stop, they would uncover high-grade ore once again.

As the years passed, it became apparent that the orebodies were trending southwest toward the Irish Mag claim. Phelps Dodge owned all the claims up to the Irish Mag, but refused to pay that site's $550,000 asking price. No copper ore had been uncovered on the claim thus far. In 1899 the newly formed Calumet and Arizona Mining Company took control of the Irish Mag claim and in 1903, opened its smelter in the nearby town of Douglas. Soon Phelps Dodge did the same and Bisbee was rid of the stench and smoke from

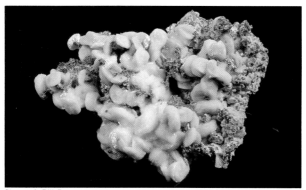

Sharon & Bill Panczner   CALCITE ON MALACHITE

the smelter. In 1931, Calumet and Arizona merged with Phelps Dodge, giving the latter almost complete control of the mines of Bisbee and the Warren Mining District. In the 1920s an open pit mine was begun on Sacramento Hill. Now Phelps Dodge operated both above and below ground. In the late 1970s mining stopped due to the economics of copper prices, but in more than a 90-year period, the district's mines produced more than $6-billion in metals.

The list of minerals from Bisbee is extensive; the more common crystallized specimens are azurite, malachite and calcite. Another mineral that has been produced from the open pit is turquoise. The turquoise, a very deep blue color, is known as Bisbee Blue. It contains a large amount of silica and takes a high polish. There are many exceedingly rare minerals found within the district's mines. Collecting is not possible, but one can take a mine tour of the Copper Queen Mine and see first hand what it was like to work beneath the Earth's surface. On occasion, mineral and lapidary clubs are allowed to collect on several of the mines' dumps. Many of the local dealers sell specimens from this location.

R.H. Perrill   AZURITE

Sharon & Bill Panczner

QUARTZ (JAPANESE TWIN) WITH CALCITE

WASHINGTON CAMP REGION

This old Spanish mining area, located on the border of Mexico and Arizona, dates back into the early 1700s. In the early 1860s, the future state of Arizona was a southern territory. Regional silver/lead mines were reportedly selling their products to the Confederate States to be used for bullets and coinage. Because of this metal trade, the Union forces came into the region and drove out the Rebels. Northern forces even arrested and sent one mine owner to prison for selling his silver and lead to the South.

This area is filled with thousands of mines and prospects, most of them dating back to the early 1800s and operated sporadically through the early 1960s. Some of the more famous mines are the Flux, Trench, Holland, Hardshell, Pride of the West and Mowry. The dumps from this area provide a good source of specimens for the collector. The Holland Mine dump has yielded some of Arizona's best quartz crystals. Found in a twin form called a Japanese twin, they appear as flattened opaque quartz crystals often over a foot long. The Mexican miners referred to them as rabbit ears. These types of twin quartz are very rare and this is one of the best locations in the United States for them.

The hill where the Holland Mine is located has many quartz prospects and is worth the time and effort to explore. Do close all gates and respect posted

Sharon & Bill Panczner   CERUSSITE

property; permission can usually be obtained in the small community of Washington Camp.

Located in Flux Canyon is the Flux Mine, a lead/silver producer which, in the upper mine workings, has yielded outstanding crystals of cerussite. These white crystals are the size of wooden matches and are called "jack straws" because of their formation on the matrix. These very fragile specimens can now be obtained only from collections or from mineral dealers because the mine is totally sealed. The Flux Mine dumps have been reworked so much that they now yield nothing of interest.

Just north of the town of Patagonia is a wash where a small prospect has recently yielded large crystals of reddish brown vanadinite. Crystals an inch or larger can be found on matrix specimens nearly six inches in diameter.

ARIVACA AREA

This area, just north of the Mexican border, is similar to the mines of Washington Camp in its production of minerals and metals. The Spanish discovered minerals here in the late 1700s and early 1800s, most development taking place in the mid 1860s to early 1900s. The main mining area is around the ghost town of Ruby. Here the Montana, Oro Blanco, Austerlitz, Yellow Jacket and American Flag Mines produced ores that yielded lead, silver and zinc. Collecting now is limited because much of the area is posted. Minerals that are easily found include quartz, calcite, pyrite and galena. Occasionally specimens of water-clear scheelite crystals have been found.

Sharon & Bill Panczner   WULFENITE

THE SANTA RITA MOUNTAINS

This mountain range, located south and east of
Tucson, contains several old mining districts and ghost
towns. Many of these mines date back to the late 1700s
and early 1800s, discovered by the Spanish when this
was part of Mexico. The mines have yielded silver, lead,
gold and copper; the latter had little interest until many
years later. Streams and washes within this mountain
range were worked in the late 1800s and early 1900s for
placer (free) gold. Mining camps such as Greaterville
and Kentucky Camp became common names during
that time.

At the southwestern end of the mountains is the
Glove or Sunrise Mine. This lead/silver mine has
produced some of Arizona's finest wulfenite crystals,
some over six inches across. They vary from an orange-
yellow to a pale yellow. Specimens in the late 1950s and
early 1960s were among the finest ever found in the
world. Some of the matrix specimens are two to three
feet in diameter and are fully covered with one to two
inch crystals. This mine is now closed and the dumps
have been reworked so many times that they will not
produce specimens. But many local collectors and
mineral dealers have specimens from the old finds for
sale or trade. Recently several specimens of wire gold
nearly 1-1/2 inches in length came on the market.
These had been found in the Greaterville area in the
early 1900s.

Sharon & Bill Panczner   MALACHITE

Conclusion

Arthur Flagg in his book, *Mineralogical Journeys in Arizona* wrote the following list of rules for collectors:

"*DON'T* fail to recognize the fact that a great many areas in Arizona are privately owned. There are still many square miles of Government owned land on which one may collect. If there are indications that the land may be privately owned, at least try to determine the facts and obtain permission to enter.

DON'T expect the large mining companies to give you a personally conducted tour through the mine which would disrupt the operating schedule.

DON'T expect large mines to supply you with a complete suite of specimens from the mine.

DON'T venture too far from well traveled roads without making inquiry locally as to conditions and where the road leads.

DON'T leave gates open through fenced lands. Neither should you make your own gate by destroying sections of the fence.

DON'T camp in the bed of a dry wash. In an hour it can become a raging torrent even though skies are clear. Camp on high ground and leave a clean camp-site. You may see such a sign as this in your travels: "This is God's country, don't make it look like Hell." Good advice.

DON'T travel without a good supply of drinking water. Beware of water issuing from old tunnels.

DON'T fail to respect the rights of others; be courteous. Courtesy will take you where brashness

45

Sharon & Bill Panczner   WULFENITE

might restrain you. Be cautious and enjoy your trip.
Mental alertness is as important as material equipment. It is a quality which some people never acquire
and many others leave at home at the very time it
would be most useful. Be cautious! The cautious
collector returns from his trip happy and in sound
condition, 'all in one piece' so to speak."

It must be remembered that when you visit a mine,
new or old, safety is of greatest importance. NEVER
go into a mine! Even mine dumps can be dangerous,
one must exercise caution. There is no room for
horseplay. It also must be remembered that you are out
in nature, so all those creepy crawlies are part of the
environment. You are in their territory! Be careful for
some of them are extremely poisonous or venomous to
humans. Even a small spider can cause great pain,
discomfort and even death.

Before going into the field, one must carefully pack
the needed equipment. The following is a list of basics
to which you can add your own suggestions:

rock hammer	prybar
sledge	chisels
crack hammer	safety glasses
whisk broom	hard hat
kleenix/toilet paper	boxes/bags
flashlight	backpack
first aid kit	hand lens
maps/books	insect repellent
binoculars	camera
rain gear	water
appropriate outdoor clothing	sunscreen

R.H. Perrill   WULFENITE

INDEX OF MINERALS PICTURED

* Arizona-Sonora Desert Museum

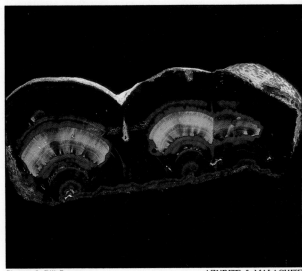

Sharon & Bill Panczner   AZURITE & MALACHITE

$4.95

Other titles from the

ARIZONA
TRAVELER
GUIDEBOOKS

Wildflowers

Cactus

Parks & Monuments

Birds

Discover Arizona

Ghost Towns

Gems & Minerals

Indians

Also available from the
AMERICAN TRAVELER SERIES

COLORADO TRAVELERS
ISBN 1-55838-097-3

50495>

9 781558 380974